Published in the UK by
POWERFRESH Limited
3 Gray Street
Northampton
NN1 3QQ

Telephone 01604 30996
Facsimile 01604 21013

D0351331

Cover and interior layout by Powerfresh

ISBN 1 874125 643

Printed in the UK by Avalon Print Northampton
Powerfresh January 1997

CONGRATULATIONS!

YOU'VE FINALLY REACHED THE BIG FOUR-OH, THE NEXT GREAT MILESTONE IN YOUR LIFE! REMEMBER THE FIRST ONE, YOUR 18TH? STILL FEEL EIGHTEEN INSIDE, HUH? PUNCHY, RAUNCHY, IN THERE STRUTTIN' YOUR STUFF, JUST AS FIT, HEALTHY, SEXY AND ATTRACTIVE AS YOU EVER WERE ... ONLY MORE SO, BECAUSE YOU'RE MORE EXPERIENCED? FORGET IT, PAL! YOU'RE MERELY ONE MORE SAD CASUALTY OF LIFE, STARTING THAT SHORT DOWN-HILL TUMBLE INTO OLD AGE ...

"HAIRSTYLES ARE MODELLED ON SPORTS STARS EG 'THE BOBBY CHARLTON' OR THE 'IAN BOTHAM'..."

"...AN OLD PAIR OF SHOES IS FOUND IN A FORGOTTEN CUPBOARD..

"... THE REVIVAL OF T-SHIRTS THAT SAY 'HOW YOUNG AND HIP I AM' ...

"... THERE ARE CHANGES IN READING MATTER."

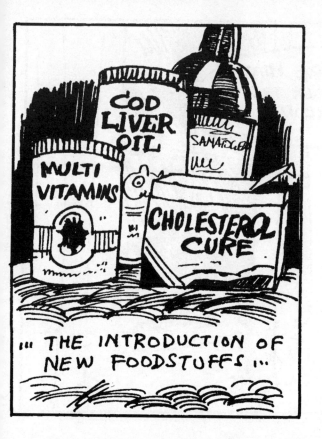

"... THE INTRODUCTION OF NEW FOODSTUFFS ..."

"... AND THE ACQUISITION OF EXERCISE MACHINES !!"

Please Send Me:

CRINKLED 'N' WRINKLED	£2.99 [ ]	THE DEFINITIVE GUIDE TO VASECTOMY	£2.99
DRIVEN CRAZY	£2.99 [ ]	KEEP FIT WITH YOUR CAT	£2.99
TRUE LOVE	£2.99 [ ]	MARITAL BLISS AND OTHER OXYMORONS	£2.99
IT'S A BOY	£2.99 [ ]	THE OFFICE FROM HELL	£2.99
IT'S A GIRL	£2.99 [ ]	PMT CRAZED	£2.99
NOW WE ARE 40	£2.99 [ ]	SEXY CROTCHWORD PUZZLES	£2.99
FUNNY SIDE OF 30s	£2.99 [ ]	STONED AGE MAN	£2.99
FUNNY SIDE OF 40 HIM	£2.99 [ ]	OUT TO LUNCH	£2.99
FUNNY SIDE OF 40 HER	£2.99 [ ]	HORNY MAN'S ADULT DOODLE BOOK	£2.50
FUNNY SIDE OF 50 HIM	£2.99 [ ]	HORNY GIRL'S ADULT DOODLE BOOK	£2.50
FUNNY SIDE OF 50 HER	£2.99 [ ]	IF BABIES COULD TALK	£2.99
FUNNY SIDE OF 60'S	£2.99 [ ]	CAT CRAZY	£2.99
FUNNY SIDE OF SEX	£2.99 [ ]	MAD TO TRAVEL BY AIR...	£2.99
FLYING FUNNIES	£2.99 [ ]	MAD TO PLAY GOLF...	£2.99
SEX IS...	£2.99 [ ]	MAD TO HAVE A BABY...	£2.99
FOOTNOTES	£2.99 [ ]	MAD TO GET MARRIED...	£2.99
SPLAT	£2.99 [ ]	MAD TO HAVE A PONY	£2.99
PEEPING TOM	£2.99 [ ]	MAD TO HAVE A CAT	£2.99
MIDLIFE CRISIS	£2.99 [ ]	MAD TO HAVE A COMPUTER	£2.99
WE'RE GETTING MARRIED	£2.99 [ ]	HE DOESN'T HAVE TO BE MAD TO BE 40	£2.99
THE ART OF SLOBOLOGY	£2.99 [ ]	SHE DOESN'T HAVE TO BE MAD TO BE 40	£2.99

I have enclosed cheque / postal order for £ .... made payable to **GUNNERS**
NAME..ADDRESS..
....
COUNTY...POSTCODE...
Please return to: **Powerfresh Ltd. 3 Gray Street, Northampton, NN1 3QQ, ENGLAND.**
EEC countries add £1 Postage, Packaging & Order processing. Outside EEC please add £3.00